ELFANDE

CONTACT
FOOD & DRINK
PHOTOGRAPHERS

11th
EDITION

Publisher
Nick Gould

Published by Elfande Ltd
Surrey House
31 Church Street
Leatherhead
Surrey KT22 8EF
England

T + 44 (0)1372 220 330
F + 44 (0)1372 220 340
E mail@contact-uk.com
W www.contact-uk.com

Contact Food & Drink Photographers 11
ISBN No:
1-905727-04-6
978-1-905727-04-09

Front Cover Image
Stephen Conroy

Production & Online Services
Robert Enstone • Suzy Woolston • Dave Millar

Sales
Wendy Jones • Matt O'Neill

Financial Director
Val Crabtree

Finance, Administration & Distribution
Julia Collyer

Printed and bound in China,
through World Print Ltd Hong Kong

Required scanning and retouching by CONTACT

Successful food photography requires good photographers, stylists, home economists, studios, props, the right location, – and this book has them all. Over 100 pages of food photography, complemented by a comprehensive range of photographic services.

Working alongside the book is our specialist food photography website **www.FoodPhotographers.com** which features the work of only food photographers and food related photographic services (including all of the contributors to this book). Each photographer has an online portfolio of 12 images on this site, alongside their contact details, and every service available has an example of their work with contact details and information about their service.

If you have difficulty contacting any of the contributors in our books please do not hesitate to phone or fax the publishers.

Also published in our specialist series alongside the Food & Drink book is Contact Interiors & Exteriors Photographers. Should you or your colleagues who commission Food & Drink or Interior & Exterior photography require further copies, please contact us and we shall try to oblige, until stocks run out.

To all users of Contact

Due to the increasing use of computers, in-house scanning and colour photocopiers, we feel it necessary to point out that every time a copy of any image is taken from this book or our online book you must have the author's permission.

All our contributors understand that sometimes to secure work from your clients, ideas, visuals and dummies have to be produced very quickly and the ideal solution can often be found within these pages! To some of you who don't always do it, please phone the contributor directly for permission.

IF WE CAN HELP STOP COPYRIGHT ABUSE – WE SHALL!

Images by:
Cover: Stephen Conroy (p32–33)
Ice: Dazeley (p34–35)

Foodphotographers.com

is our dedicated food photography site incorporating all Contact book and web contributors who specialise in the realms of food & drink. Photographers, stylists, home economists, props & studios for hire are all included, with images to demonstrate their work as well as contact details & any other relevant information. You can find this book available to view on the internet right now!

Contact A Creative

The ContactACreative.com site offers a comprehensive range of information on creatives and their services. Apart from the portfolios of photographers, you are able to view imagery from illustrators and designers as well as find listings on other services and their facilities. All in all, a one stop shop for all your creative needs.

The Law

Copyright © 2006 Nicholas Gould

Contact Details Key

- **T** Telephone
- **F** Fax
- **M** Mobile
- **P** Pager
- **IS** ISDN
- **T/F** Telephone/Fax
- **E** Email
- **W** Web Address

FOODPHOTOGRAPHERS.COM

Contact A Creative

COMPREHENSIVE SOURCE WEBSITE FOR ARTBUYERS

CONTENTS

FOOD & DRINK
PHOTOGRAPHERS

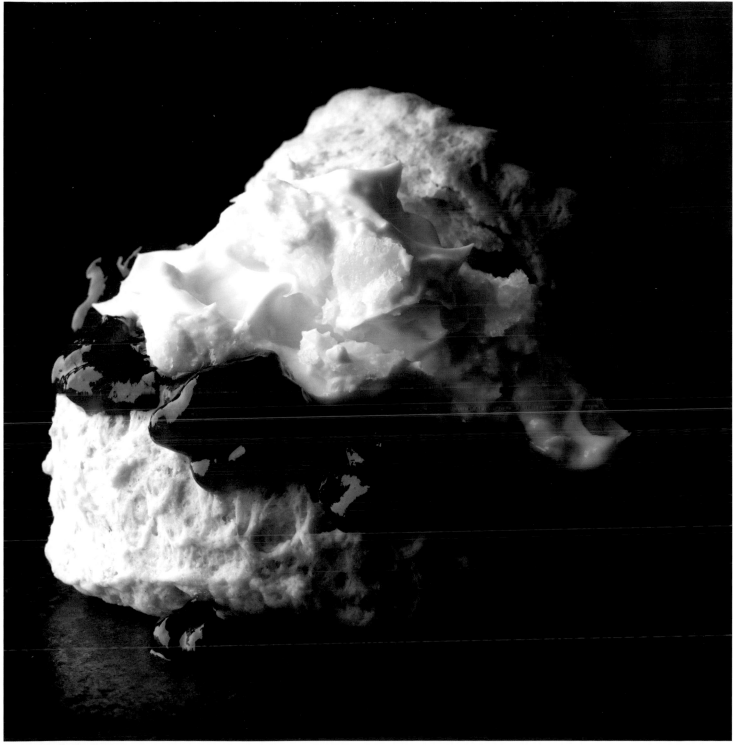

Food Stylist: Kerenza Harries

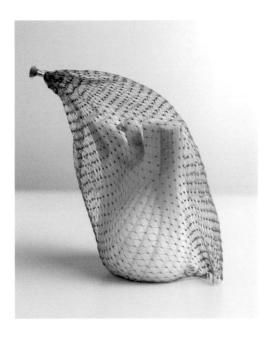  

Home economist: Elaine Ngan

Clive Bozzard-Hill

Represented by Rosie Beckett : **T** + 44 (0)20 8255 1574   **M** + 44 (0)7973 193 071
E *rosiebeckett@mac.com*   **W** *www.bozza-uk.com*
W *www.foodphotographers.com/CliveBozzardHill*

18

22

Random House

Maison Blanc Vite

Waitrose premium coffee range

T + 44 (0)20 7253 2863   **F** + 44 (0)20 7553 7740
E nick@nickcarman.com   **W** www.nickcarman.com

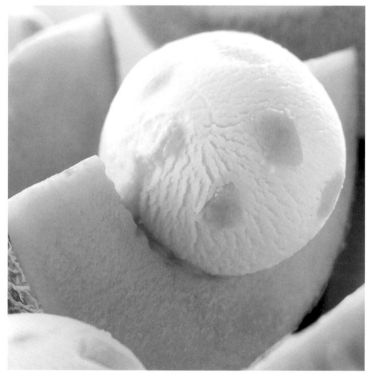

Peter Cassidy

☎ + 44 (0)20 7258 0705 📱 + 44 (0)7976 739 915 ✉ petecassidy@excite.com

Peter Cassidy

☎ + 44 (0)20 7258 0705   📱 + 44 (0)7976 739 915   ✉ petecassidy@excite.com

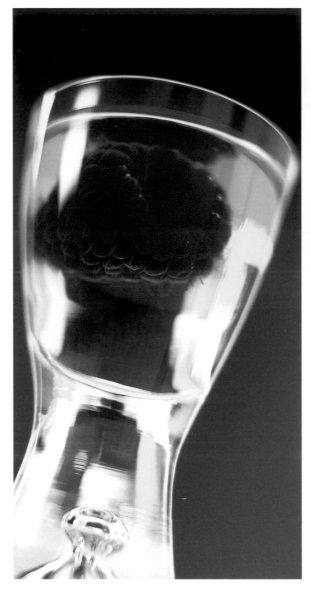

T + 44 (0)20 7736 3171   **F** + 44 (0)20 7371 8876
E studio@peterdazeley.com   **W** www.peterdazeley.com
Represented by: Sarah Ryder Richardson: **T** + 44 (0)20 7736 2999

after a
meal

It's good to drink 8 glasses of water a day- when it's our spring water from near the Andelle River in France, it's easy!

YOUR M&S

T + 44 (0)113 262 8811   **F** + 44 (0)113 262 8822   **M** + 44 (0)7976 766 256
E john@johneckart.co.uk   **W** www.johneckart.co.uk

Tesco's Organic range

British Airways

Del Monte Quality

fresh

BREAKFAST BERRIES
WITH YOGURT & MUESLI

Apple and mixed berries with Greek
yogurt & honey and crunchy muesli

serving suggestion

Food Stylist: Steven Wheeler

Amanda Heywood

☎ + 44 (0)20 8749 9911   📠 + 44 (0)20 8740 5111   📱 + 44 (0)7831 751 712

✉ amanda@food-photography.co.uk   🌐 www.amandaheywood.co.uk

Food Stylist: Oona van den Berg

Sue Hiscoe

T + 44 (0)1422 824 422   **F** + 44 (0)1422 824 433
E sue@suehiscoe.co.uk   **W** www.suehiscoe.co.uk

All images shown from Annabel Karmels After School Meal Planner: Published by Ebury Press

Dave King

☎ + 44 (0)870 754 0901   📱 + 44 (0)7801 492 641
✉ mail@davekingsstudio.co.uk   🌐 www.davekingsstudio.co.uk

All images shown from Annabel Karmels After School Meal Planner: Published by Ebury Press

Laurence Hudghton Photography

T + 44 (0)161 272 7977   **W** www.hudghtonphotography.co.uk
E laurence@hudghtonphotography.co.uk   **E** phil@hudghtonphotography.co.uk

Sarah Jane Leggett

☎ + 44 (0)20 7323 6606   🖷 + 44 (0)20 7636 6606
✉ laura@chrisbiggs.co.uk   🌐 www.chrisbiggs.co.uk

Home economist: Bethany Heald

Duncan Loughrey

T + 44 (0)1582 483 828   F + 44 (0)1582 455 089   M + 44 (0)7971 193 921

E duncan@millyard.co.uk   W www.millyard.co.uk

Stuart MacGregor

T + 44 (0)20 7388 9652   M + 44 (0)7971 820 384

E stuartmacgregor@btclick.com   W www.foodphotographers.com/StuartMacGregor

T + 44 (0)20 7498 2399   **F** + 44 (0)20 7498 2238
E alan@newnhamphoto.co.uk   **W** www.newnhamphoto.co.uk

Ian O'Leary

T + 44 (0)20 7580 3306   **E** oleary@dircon.co.uk
W www.oleary.dircon.co.uk   **W** www.contact-me.net/IanO'Leary

Art Director: Paul Reed, Cobalt ID • Food Stylist: Gizzi

Lis Parsons

T + 44 (0)7932 013 751   E lis@lisparsonsphotography.co.uk   W www.lisparsonsphotography.co.uk

Graham Precey

T + 44 (0)20 8762 9993 F + 44 (0)20 8762 9994

E graham@precey.com W www.precey.com

W www.contact-me.net/GrahamPrecey

Gareth Sambidge

Represented @ Process ☎ + 44 (0)20 7277 8400   📱 + 44 (0)7950 311 425
✉ kim@processphotography.com   🌐 www.processphotography.com

Toby Scott

T + 44 (0)20 8749 5888   **M** + 44 (0)7961 189 709
E toby@tobyscottphotography.com   **W** www.tobyscottphotography.com

Food Stylist: Lynne Clayton • Agency: Design Bridge • Client: Chicken Tonight

Client: Gyro International for Tate & Lyle; Food Stylist: Kathy Man

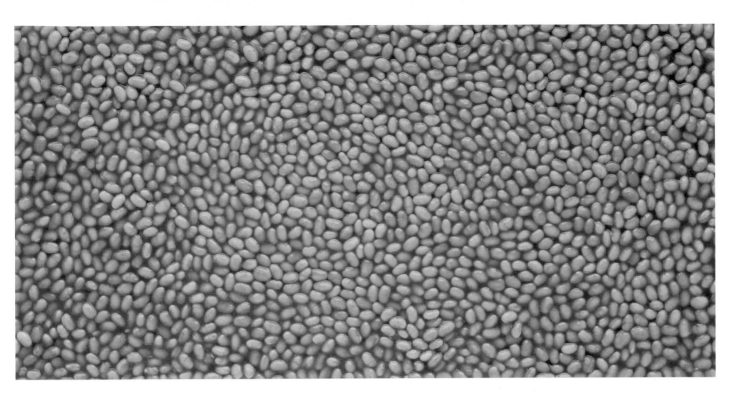

Client: Hovis; Food Stylist: Peta O'Brien

Client: Costa • Food Styling: Eliza Baird

Andrew Sydenham

T + 44 (0)20 7207 1957 M + 44 (0)7831 756 866

E sydphoto@mac.com W www.contact-me.net/AndrewSydenham

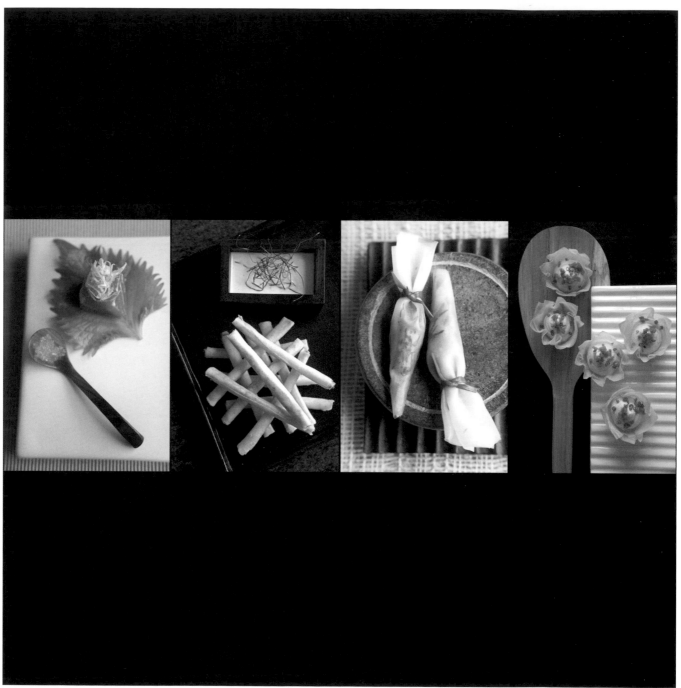

Recipes and food styling by Eico Kano

106

Craig Fraser

Craig Fraser

FOOD & DRINK
SERVICES

FOOD STYLISTS &
HOME ECONOMISTS

Sandra Baddeley

Photographer: Frank Adam

London
UK

M + 44 (0)7860 390 381
E sandra.baddeley@btinternet.com
W www.sandra.baddeley.btinternet.co.uk

Food Stylist and Recipe Writer of 19 years experience in conventional and digital photography for editorial, packaging, promotional media and advertising.

Specialising in close-up work with precise attention to detail offering innovative solutions to create the highest possible standards.

Extensive database of suppliers for the widest range of food, herbal and aromatherapy props.

Clients include: Foxes, Heinz, Marks & Spencer, Quaker, RHM, Sainsbury's, Tesco, Traidcraft, Waitrose.

Eliza Baird

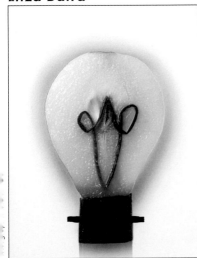

Client: tesco.com

HERS Agency Ltd
UK

T + 44 (0)870 429 6499
F + 44 (0)1884 855 855
E hers@hersagency.co.uk
W www.hersagency.co.uk

Contact: Julia

Experienced in all aspects of Food Styling: advertising, packaging, editorial and TV commercials. Also develops recipes for editorial and PR.

Modern, creative style.
Happy to work abroad.

Clients include: Tesco, M&S, Lloyd Grossman, Cathedral City, Waitrose, Costa Coffee, Debenhams, Morrisons, Waitrose, New Holland Publishing, TGI Friday, Compass, Redwood Publishing, P&O, Sainsbury's, National Magazines.

Wendy Barrie

Photographer: Graham Lees

Drumsheugh Toll, 1 Belford Road
Edinburgh EH4 3BL, UK

T + 44 (0)131 220 3630
M + 44 (0)7802 426 205
E wendy@wendybarrie.co.uk
W www.scottishfoodguide.com
W www.wendybarrie.co.uk

Good Food Champion, Director of award-winning Scottish Food Guide and Education Convener for Slow Food, Edinburgh Convivium, specialising in… Food Tourism: quality assurance, marketing, personal appearances and media contributions. Food Events: cookery presenter, project management and media handling for food festivals, UK events and exhibitions. Food Education and Hygiene: commissioned recipe writing, course development, healthy eating and hygiene training. Food Styling: still and video, studio and location. Seaside studio kitchen available for hire.

Jacqueline Bellefontaine

Photographer: Dave Jordan

Food Stylist and Cookery writer with extensive experience in all areas of food photography.

Regularly commissioned for food styling and recipe development for magazines, books, supermarkets and PR companies.

Member of the Guild of Food Writers, author of fifteen cookery books and contributor to various magazines.

224 Long Lane
London SE1 4QB
UK

T + 44 (0)20 7407 5552
M + 44 (0)7973 333 885
E info@jacquelinebellefontaine.co.uk
W www.jacquelinebellefontaine.co.uk

Jennie Berresford

Photographer: Paul Williams

Client: Chicago Town Pizzas

HERS Agency Ltd
UK

T + 44 (0)870 429 6499
F + 44 (0)1884 855 855
E hers@hersagency.co.uk
W www.hersagency.co.uk

Contact: Julia

Food Stylist/Home Economist, very experienced in advertising, packaging, TV Commercials and editorial. Specialises in fish products, ice-cream and pizzas.

Clients include: Waitrose, Tesco, Sainsbury's, M&S, Burger King, Uncle Ben's, Divertimenti, Safeway, Chicago Town, McDougalls.

Jo Brewer

Red Photography Ltd

Honeysuckle Cottage
6 Lin'fit Fold
Linthwaite
Huddersfield HD7 5LW
UK

M + 44 (0)7778 314 373

Freelance Home Economist.

Extensive experience in all aspects of food photography.

Brian Brooke

Walker Brow Farm
Macclesfield Road
Whaley Bridge
Derbyshire SK23 7DR
UK

T + 44 (0)1663 735 212
F + 44 (0)1663 733 616
M + 44 (0)7798 521 269
E Brian.Brooke@btinternet.com

Food Stylist/Home Economist

Extensive experience in preparing and styling for magazine, TV, film and food packaging. Wide experience in recipe development, writing and testing.

Clients include: Asda, Morrisons, Amoy, Lea & Perrins, Fayrefield Foods, Weightwatchers, Cheshire Smokehouse, Caterforce, Farmhouse Fare, The Village Bakery, Dale pack, Kenco, Iceland, William Murray, Marks & Spencer and Dairycrest.

Available for work within the UK and abroad.

Anna Burges-Lumsden

HERS Agency Ltd
UK

☏ + 44 (0)870 429 6499
🖷 + 44 (0)1884 855 855
✉ hers@hersagency.co.uk
🌐 www.hersagency.co.uk

Contact: Julia

Up and coming, creative Food Stylist and Food Writer, working in Editorial, PR and Television. Also Recipe Development and Feature writing.

Clients include: Olive, Delicious, Real, BBC Good Food, Sunday Express Magazine, Woman & Home, Closer, Match.

Kit Chan

HERS Agency Ltd
UK

☏ + 44 (0)870 429 6499
🖷 + 44 (0)1884 855 855
✉ hers@hersagency.co.uk
🌐 www.hersagency.co.uk

Contact: Julia

Creative Food Stylist working on brochures, advertising, recipe development and editorial. Has an extensive knowledge of world food.

Languages: Cantonese

Clients include: Delicious, BBC Good Food Magazine, M&S Magazine, Eve Magazine.

Jayne Cross

5 The Avenue
Loughton
Essex IG10 4PT
UK

☏ + 44 (0)20 8418 7844
📱 + 44 (0)7808 885 618
✉ jayne@jaynecross.com
🌐 www.jaynecross.com

Creative and adaptable Food Stylist and Cookery Writer with experience in styling for magazines, packaging and websites.

A member of the Guild of Food Writers and experienced in both recipe development and testing.

Clients include: Waitrose Food Illustrated, Waitrose Seasons, BBC Good Food, uktv, Publicis Blueprint, Marks and Spencer, BBCi.

Ailsa Cruickshank

Photographer: Steve Payne

Client: Tesco

HERS Agency Ltd
UK

☏ + 44 (0)870 429 6499
🖷 + 44 (0)1884 855 855
✉ hers@hersagency.co.uk
🌐 www.hersagency.co.uk

Contact: Julia

Creative Food Stylist, working in editorial, PR, packaging and advertising. Equally happy with recipes or product. Specialises in cakes and ice-cream.

Clients include: Green Isle, Tesco, Sainsbury's, RHM, Budgens, British Airways, Little Chef, Tival

Pippa Cuthbert

Photographer: Stuart West

Client: New Holland Publishing

HERS Agency Ltd
UK

☎ + 44 (0)870 429 6499
📠 + 44 (0)1884 855 855
✉ hers@hersagency.co.uk
🌐 www.hersagency.co.uk

Contact: Julia

Creative Food stylist and Food Writer,
working in editorial, PR, packaging,
advertising and TV commercials. Pippa
has co-written 6 books and also enjoys
recipe development and writing for
magazines.

Clients include: Olive Magazine, Delicious,
New Holland Publishing, Tesco, Kenwood,
Sainsbury, Boots, Sunday Times Style
Magazine, Lurpak, Co-Op, Aldi, M&S
Magazine, Saturday Telegraph, The
Independent, Bernard Matthews, M&S,
Kinsmill, Cassell Illustrated, Hamlyn,
National Magazines, Cuisine Magazine
(NZ).

Siân Davies

Photographer: Tony Briscoe

Home Economist/food stylist/cookery
writer.

Wide experience in editorial and packaging
food styling.

Also recipe development and writing for
magazines, cookery books and PR products

5 Hyde Close
Harpenden
Hertfordshire AL5 4NB
UK

☎ + 44 (0)1582 462 680
📱 + 44 (0)7850 883 387
✉ sianidavis@aol.com

Martha Dunkerley

Photographer: Ben Edwards

HERS Agency Ltd
UK

☎ + 44 (0)870 429 6499
📠 + 44 (0)1884 855 855
✉ hers@hersagency.co.uk
🌐 www.hersagency.co.uk

Contact: Julia

Creative Food Stylist/Home Economist
working in editorial, packaging,
advertising. Equally at home with product
or recipes.

Clients include: Sainsbury's, KFC,
Unilever, Walls, Heinz, Waitrose,
Green Ilse, Quorn, Tesco, Dolmio,
Somerfield, Gü, Abbey National, Unilever,
Co-Op, Carte D'Or, Quorn, Whirlpool,
Budgens, BBC Promotions.

Gizzi Erskine

Photographer: William Lingwood

Client: Tesco

HERS Agency Ltd
UK

☎ + 44 (0)870 429 6499
📠 + 44 (0)1884 855 855
✉ hers@hersagency.co.uk
🌐 www.hersagency.co.uk

Contact: Julia

Versatile Food Writer and Food Stylist,
with a passion for food and a fresh,
modern and innovative style.

Food styling for Editorial, Packaging,
PR and Advertising for both Stills and
Commercials, as well as food writing,
recipe development and TV presenting.

Clients include: Elle(USA), Tesco,
Weetabix, Uncle Ben's, Slimfast, Olive,
Men's Fitness, Living Etc, Uncle Ben's,
Sky 1 "Taste" (regular presenter), Slimfast
Sunday Express Magazine, Lurpak, Lyles,
Ryvita, Living Etc, Forward Publishing.
BBC Good Food, National Magazines,
Easy Living.

Clare Ferguson

Client: Homes & Gardens

Extremely experienced & creative Food Stylist, working worldwide in TV commercials, Advertising, PR and Editorial. A member of the Guild of Foodwriters, Clare has written many books, and regularly writes features for magazines. Extensive knowledge of world food. Food consultant to major food manufacturers/supermarkets, for product development and research.

Clients include: Noon, Hilton UK & Ireland, Homes & Gardens, Marks & Spencer, Birds Eye Walls, Liptons, Ryland Peters & Small, Kraft, Carte D'Or, Sainsburys', Liptons, The Guardian, Hovis, Prestige, Flora, Stouffers (USA), Carte D'Or, Knorr, Pret A Manger.

HERS Agency Ltd
UK

☎ + 44 (0)870 429 6499
🖷 + 44 (0)1884 855 855
✉ hers@hersagency.co.uk
🌐 www.hersagency.co.uk

Contact: Julia

Nicola Fowler

Photographer: Chris Knaggs

Client: Tesco

Food Writer and creative Food Stylist working in stills advertising, packaging, brochures and editorial; Experienced in recipe development and writing articles for editorial, brochures and PR.

Very versatile with a positive approach to problem-solving.

Clients include: Allied Domecq, Sharwoods, Waitrose, Sainsbury's, Somerfield, Birds Eye Walls, Wetherspoons, Tesco, Kelloggs, Youngs Brewery, Quaker.

HERS Agency Ltd
UK

☎ + 44 (0)870 429 6499
🖷 + 44 (0)1884 855 855
✉ hers@hersagency.co.uk
🌐 www.hersagency.co.uk

Contact: Julia

Marina Filippelli

Flat 2
69 Dartmouth Road
London NW2 4EP
UK

📱 + 44 (0)7771 783 996
✉ food@marinafilippelli.com
🌐 www.marinafilippelli.com

I have been food editor of Essentials and Tesco Magazines and in the past year have contributed to numerous magazine titles, including BBC Good Food, Waitrose Food Illustrated, Ideal Home, Essentials, Tesco Magazine and Family Circle. As well as feature writing and food styling, some clients call on my experience as food editor to plan and produce their cookery pages and supplements. In 2005 I was involved in a successful pitch for River Publishing; I was responsible for developing the blueprint for Irresistible, a new Weight-Watchers magazine. I have also worked as a home economist on packaging for Sainsbury's and have two new books due to be published: Fresh Italian, Hamlyn (September 2006) and Steam Cuisine, Ebury (early 2007).

Christine Greaves

Photographer: Myles New

Client: Seven Publishing

HERS Agency Ltd
UK

☎ + 44 (0)870 429 6499
🖷 + 44 (0)1884 855 855
✉ hers@hersagency.co.uk
🌐 www.hersagency.co.uk

Contact: Julia

Extremely experienced, creative Food Stylist, working worldwide in advertising, TV commercials, packaging, brochures and editorial.

Clients include: Waitrose, Wild Bean Café, M&S, Tesco, Thames TV, Asda, Walls, Kraft, Thorntons, Heinz, Knorr, Pizza Hut, Lea & Perrins, Sainsbury's, Burger King, Boots.

Feature films include: Notting Hill, Chocolat, Onegin, Portait of a Lady, The Constant Gardener, Hitchhiker's Guide To The Galaxy.

Carole Handslip

Photographer: Mike Cooper

Client: Somerfield

HERS Agency Ltd
UK

☎ + 44 (0)870 429 6499
📠 + 44 (0)1884 855 855
📧 hers@hersagency.co.uk
🌐 www.hersagency.co.uk

Contact: Julia

Very experienced, creative Food Stylist for stills advertising, packaging, brochures, and editorial. A member of the Guild of Foodwriters, Carole has written numerous books and works regularly on recipe development for PR and Advertorial.

Clients include: Knorr, Waitrose, Somerfield, Sainsbury's, Lloyd Grossman, BP, Kingsmill, Heinz, Ryvita, National Magazines, Asda, Denham Productions/Tesco

Lizzie Harris

Photographer: Jon Whitaker

32 Allington Road
London W10 4AY
UK

☎ + 44 (0)7976 434 224
📧 hellolizzie@aol.com

Food stylist, writer and creative recipe developer with wide experience in editorial publishing and PR.

Also a regular chef and assistant teacher with Tasting Places cookery courses throughout Italy specialising in regional Italian cuisine.

Regular clients include: Sunday Times, House Beautiful, Good Food, Tesco, 'She', National Magazine, Starbucks, Carroll & Brown Publishers, Kyle Cathie.

Seiko Hatfield

UK

☎ + 44 (0)7813 857 634
📧 mail@seikohatfield.co.uk
🌐 www.seikohatfield.co.uk

As you might expect from a Tokyo trained stylist, I am an expert in Asian and oriental food. My experience in award winning British restaurants also allows me to feel at home working for clients that include SuperCook, Warburtons and Weight Watchers.

In addition to commercial and editorial styling, I enjoy recipe development and am happy to undertake assignments in London or the north.

Kathryn Hawkins

Photographer: Stuart MacGregor

Client: SuperCook

UK

📱 + 44 (0)7831 127 281
📧 kathrynhk@aol.com

Based in central Scotland, Kathryn Hawkins is an experienced cookery writer and food stylist. She has worked for many women's magazines and in advertising and PR. Interests include cakes, baking, casual dining, regional food and healthy eating.

A member of the Guild of Food Writers, Kathryn has written many books and recent projects include Smoothies and Juices, Pancakes, Bread, and Fruit.

Recent clients include: SuperCook, New Holland Publishers, Chrysalis Publishing, Nick Nairn, Oui 3 Design, Eagle Moss.

thany Heald

HERS Agency Ltd
UK

T + 44 (0)870 429 6499
F + 44 (0)1884 855 855
E hers@hersagency.co.uk
W www.hersagency.co.uk

Contact: Julia

Creative and versatile Food Stylist working in editorial, packaging, advertising, TV Commercials, Feature Films & TV programmes.

Recipe writing and development.

Clients include: Masterchef/BBC2, Ready Steady Cook, BBC Holby City, UK Food, Conran Octopus, World's Greatest Dish/Sky, BBC Books, Mitchell Beazley, Coca-Cola, M&S, Tesco, Morrisons, Select Magazine, Unilever, Dorling Kindersley, Sunday Express Magazine, Tesco.

Nicole Herft

Photographer: Tony Briscoe

Up and coming creative Food Stylist working in editorial, packaging, and television.

A qualified head chef, with wide knowledge of world food and also experienced in recipe development and testing.

Clients include: Compass Group, Cathedral City Cheese, Dorling Kindersley, Sainsbury's Magazine, Prospect Pictures (Great Food Live, Saturday Cooks, Sunday Feast, Taste).

HERS Agency Ltd
UK

T + 44 (0)870 429 6499
F + 44 (0)1884 855 855
E hers@hersagency.co.uk
W www.hersagency.co.uk

Contact: Julia

Photographer: Chris Leah

Emma Kaye

The Hollies
Market Rasen Road
Holton le Moor
Lincolnshire LN7 6AE
UK

T + 44 (0)1673 828 049
M + 44 (0)7774 211 299
E food@emmakaye.co.uk
W www.emmakaye.co.uk

Creative, friendly Home Economist specialising in all types of food work, preparation of food for photography, recipe development for food retailers, writing of cooking instructions for food packaging, food presentations, demonstrations and a successful cooking for kids class.

Portfolio available on request.

Travel not a problem.

aire Kelsey

Photographer: Peter Chambers

Client: Lundy's Foods

Northwest
UK

☎ + 44 (0)7980 628 868
🌐 www.clairekelsey.co.uk

Versatile style, happy with precise technical
work with product for packaging as well as
a more relaxed style for editorial matter.

Imaginative approach, enjoy creative
problem solving.

Wide database of suppliers for
foodstuffs and kitchen locations.

Asda, Morrisons, Kenwood, Portmeirion, ITV.

Marie-Ange Lapierre

Photographer: Jean Cazals

HERS Agency Ltd
UK

☎ + 44 (0)870 429 6499
📠 + 44 (0)1884 855 855
✉ hers@hersagency.co.uk
🌐 www.hersagency.co.uk

Contact: Julia

Creative Food Stylist, experienced in
advertising, packaging, "state-of-the-art"
editorial and brochures. Wide knowledge of
world food and particularly enjoys Asian,
Italian and "fusion" cooking.
Languages: French

Clients include: Waitrose, Boots, Homes
& Gardens, Onken, Sainsbury's, Tesco,
French Vogue, Delicious, M&S, The Body
Shop, 34 Magazine, Hachette Publishing,
The Observer, Uniq, Flora, Duncan Baird
Publishing, National Magazines,
John Lewis.

Jane Lawrie

Photographer: Ken Field

UK

📱 + 44 (0)7802 652 868
✉ jane.lawrie3@ntlworld.com

Creative food stylist with loads of
experience available for advertising,
packaging and editorial photo shoots.

Development of recipes a speciality, each
one carefully created and tested to match
your specific brief.

Clients include: Amazon Publishing,
Asda, Bramley Apples, British Eggs,
Centre Parks, Filippo Berio, Kettle Chips,
Marks & Spencer, Merchant Gourmet,
Mushroom Growers, President Cheese,
Sainsbury's, Tesco, Watercress Association,
Weatherspoons.

Mary Luther

Photographer: Dave King

Client: Annabel Karmel

HERS Agency Ltd
UK

☎ + 44 (0)870 429 6499
📠 + 44 (0)1884 855 855
✉ hers@hersagency.co.uk
🌐 www.hersagency.co.uk

Contact: Julia

American born Food Stylist/Home
Economist, working on feature films,
including Harry Potter 1- 5, The Hours,
Ted & Sylvia, Proof, Thunderbirds, First
Daughter, Batman Begins, Matchpoint,
Calendar Girls, Casino Royale, Flight 93,
Atonement, The Golden Age.

Also very experienced in advertising,
packaging, brochures and PR. Specialises
in detailed work with product, particularly
cake and dessert packaging.

Her clients include: Cadbury's, Asda,
Birds Eye, Bernard Matthews, Mr.Kipling,
Sainsbury's, Tesco, Unilever, Quaker.

Caroline Marson

Client: Transworld Publishing

HERS Agency Ltd
UK

T +44 (0)870 429 6499
F +44 (0)1884 855 855
E hers@hersagency.co.uk
W www.hersagency.co.uk

Contact: Julia

Very experienced Food Stylist, Food editor and writer, working in the fields of "cutting-edge" editorial, brochures, recipe development, advertising, PR and packaging.

Clients include: Olive Magazine, Ryland Peters & Small, Transworld Publishing, Ebury Press, El Paso, tesco.com, Baileys, Intercontinental Hotels, Fortnum & Mason, Birds Eye, Harrods, Neff, Unilever, Boots, Ideal Home, Uncle Ben's, Blue Dragon, Sharwoods.

Stella Murphy

Photographer: Mike McGoran

Client: Abbey International • Agency: Tequila/London

6 High View Close
Loughton
Essex IG10 4EG
UK

T +44 (0)20 8508 2794
M +44 (0)7836 337 255
E stella.murphy@virgin.net

Wide experience in food preparation for advertising, packaging and digital photography.

TV Commercials.
Recipe development, testing and editorial.
Prepared to travel UK and abroad.

Clients include Sainsbury's, Marks & Spencer, McDonalds, Uncle Ben's, Discovery, Debenham's, Oscar Drink, New Holland Publishers, Dixy Chicken, Beefeater Gin, The Field, Herbe Pizzas, Dairy Crest, Tesco, Le Creuset, Carol Vorderman Detox Video, Hellmann's, Whistlestop, Home Pride, Lavery Rowe, Delice de France, Kettle Chips, Monarch Airlines, Vili's Pies, Abbey International, Waitrose, PEK, Broadband, John Lewis, The Hairy Bikers, Samsung, National Lottery, EasyJet.

rob morris-lang

Freelance Food Stylist / Qualified Chef - UK Based - Prepared to travel

An experienced passionate and creative food stylist with a great knowledge and love for food. Mainly working in all aspects of still-life photography from Editorial, Packaging, Advertising and TV Commercials. With his skills and ability as a trained chef he works closely with many companies in the development of recipes and writing of food articles. His attention to detail, unfailing patience and unflappable style are almost legendary with his clients.

tel: 07970 663380   email: robmorrislang@ukonline.co.uk   www.robmorrislang.com

Stephen Parkins-Knight

Photographer: Daniel Jones

Client: Smith & Gilmour/Great British Menu

HERS Agency Ltd
UK

T *+ 44 (0)870 429 6499*
F *+ 44 (0)1884 855 855*
E *hers@hersagency.co.uk*
W *www.hersagency.co.uk*

Contact: Julia

Innovative Chef, Food Consultant and Food Stylist, working in all aspects of food: Food styling and recipe development for photography in Editorial, PR, Marketing and Advertising. Consultant to major food producers, new product development, demonstrating and TV presentation.

Clients include: Sainsbury's, Sunday Express Magazine, Sunday Telegraph, Harrods, Greencore, Northern Foods, M&S, Smith & Gilmour, Eat & Two Veg Restaurant Group, Moy Park, Scotbeef, Blackstones Kitchens, Geest.

Katie Rogers

re:fresh
Suite 4
Swan Centre
Fishers Lane
London W4 1RX
UK

T *+ 44 (0)20 8747 8080*
F *+ 44 (0)20 8747 8228*
M *+ 44 (0)7767 444 223*
E *info@refresh-agency.com*
W *www.refresh-agency.com*

Home Economist/Stylist/Food Writer.

Experienced in all areas of food styling and home economist work.

Clients include:
M&S, Waitrose, Sainsbury's, Tesco, Asda, Somerfield

Lesley Sendall

Photographer: Simon Page-Ritchie

Client: Unilever/CakeMedia

HERS Agency Ltd
UK

T *+ 44 (0)870 429 6499*
F *+ 44 (0)1884 855 855*
E *hers@hersagency.co.uk*
W *www.hersagency.co.uk*

Contact: Julia

Extremely experienced Food Stylist, working primarily in Advertising, packaging and TV commercials, with an emphasis on modern, imaginative presentation, as well as "problem solving", technical proficiency and attention to detail.

Clients include:
Birds Eye, Bernard Matthews, Amoy, McDonalds, Bighams, Waitrose, Morrisons, Tesco, Gu, Napolina, Hovis, Asda, Co-Op, Hilton Hotels, Burger King, Sainsbury's, Cadbury's, Pepsodent, Colmans, Nestlé, Knorr, Daylesford Organics.

Jennie Shapter

Desborough Lodge
Walton Lane
Weybridge
Surrey KT13 8LT
UK

T *+ 44 (0)1932 843 649*
F *+ 44 (0)1932 850 815*
M *+ 44 (0)7740 468 205*
E *jennieshapter@jennieshapter.com*

A versatile and creative Food Stylist, Cookery Writer and Food Consultant.

Extensive experience in all areas of food styling for advertising, packaging, PR and editorial food photography, television commercials and videos.

A member of the Guild of Food Writers, author of over 20 books, with expertise in recipe development, writing food articles, PR literature, recipe and equipment testing.

Nicole Szabason

Contact: Julia
HERS Agency Ltd
UK

T + 44 (0)870 429 6499
F + 44 (0)1884 855 855
E hers@hersagency.co.uk
W www.hersagency.co.uk

Very experienced Food Stylist, working worldwide on TV commercials, advertising, packaging and brochures. Expertise covers all areas of food, but specialises in pizzas, ice-cream and detailed, technical work with product.

Clients include: Bernard Matthews, Carte D'Or, McVities, Schwartz, Birds Eye Walls, M&S, Knorr, Findus, Sharwoods, Green Isle, Dr.Oetker, Whiskas, Gordon's Gin, Quaker, Waitrose, Baileys, Somerfield, McDonalds, Nescafé, Tesco, Kingsmill, Asda, Mr Kipling, Sainsbury's, KFC, RHM.

Linda Tubby

12 Stuart Road
London W3 6DG
UK

T + 44 (0)20 8992 9652
M + 44 (0)7770 945 330
E on request

Food stylist and writer with wide experience styling for books and magazines, packaging, advertising and commercials.

Writes recipe features for magazines including Delicious and Food and Travel. "Spanish Country Kitchen" is her latest book, other titles include "Herbs" and "Grill".

Photographer: Peter Cassidy

Client: Meze RPS

Dagmar Vesely

Client: Homes & Gardens

HERS Agency Ltd
UK

T + 44 (0)870 429 6499
F + 44 (0)1884 855 855
E hers@hersagency.co.uk
W www.hersagency.co.uk

Contact: Julia

Creative, experienced Food Stylist, working in Stills Advertising, TV commercials, Editorial, PR and packaging. Recipe development for PR, editorial and books. Happy to work abroad. Languages: Czech.

Clients include: Hellmans, Lurpak, Prestige, Waitrose, Sainsbury's, Tesco, Heinz, Marks & Spencer, Birds Eye, Carte D'Or, Homes & Gardens, Ebury Press, In Style Magazine, Cannon Cookers, Cadbury's, Green Isle, Cathedral City.

Mari Mererid Williams

Photographer: Toby Scott

A highly experienced food stylist, working in editorial, PR and packaging. Writes and develops recipes for magazines and leaflets. Also has a natural flair for prop styling.

19 Ellesmere Road
Berkhamsted
Hertfordshire
HP4 2EX
UK

T/F + 44 (0)1442 873 190
M + 44 (0)7703 398 476
E mari@ukgateway.net

Jan Zacharias

Jan Zacharias Catering
Storeton Hall Farm
Lever Causeway
Storeton
Wirral CH63 6HT
UK

☎ + 44 (0)151 608 2352
Ⓜ + 44 (0)7885 787 752
Ⓔ janzachariascatering@hotmail.com
Ⓦ www.janzachariascatering.org.uk

Chef/Food Stylist.

Wide experience in food preparation for
photography. Specialist in large group shots
for food hamper brochures, calendars, bakeware
shots etc.

Clients include:
Bisto, Rayware, Park Foods plc,
Woodward Food Service, Meyer
and Express Dairies.

PROPS &
INTERIORS STYLISTS

Suzie Finch

Photographer: Daniel Jones

Client: 57 Pont Street Hotel

HERS Agency Ltd
UK

Ⓣ + 44 (0)870 429 6499
Ⓕ + 44 (0)1884 855 855
Ⓔ hers@hersagency.co.uk
Ⓦ www.hersagency.co.uk

Contact: Julia

Suzie is a very experienced stylist now
specialising in interiors.The luxury hotel
market has been the major part of her
recent work and she has also cultivated
skills working with flowers. She has styled
apartments aboard cruise ships – again at
the top end of the luxury market.This has
involved not only photography but also
show apartments and consultancy prior to
photographic shoots.

Clients include:
Cunard
The World
Handpicked Hotels
Grayshott Spa
The Park Bath
Marriott Hotels
Christies
Flying Flowers
Aston Martin

Liz Hippisley

29 Finlay Street
Fulham
London SW6 6HE
UK

T + 44 (0)20 7736 5856
F + 44 (0)20 7736 4633
M + 44 (0)7050 128 718
E liz@bayhippisley.com

Props stylist for food, lifestyle, interiors and locations for editorial, packaging and advertising.

Clients include: Conran Octopus, Mitchell Beazley, National Magazines, BBC, Hasbro, Sainsbury's, Abbey Bank, Alliance & Leicester, Jacobs, Nestlé etc.

Clare Hunt

Photographer: Bill Kingston

Client: Sainsbury's Magazine

HERS Agency Ltd
UK

T + 44 (0)870 429 6499
F + 44 (0)1884 855 855
E hers@hersagency.co.uk
W www.hersagency.co.uk

Contact: Julia

Very Experienced Stylist on room-sets, life-style and table-top for advertising, brochures, editorial and commercials with an emphasis on life-style and food. Happy to take on all aspects of production.

Clients include: Waitrose, Marks & Spencer, National Magazines, Sainsbury's Magazine, Redwood Publishing, BBC Good Food, Orange, John Lewis, Twinings, Debenhams, Octopus Publishing.

Rosie Hopper Styling

Client: Wickes

UK

I am a stylist with extensive experience. I have been presented with projects both diverse and varied encompassing food; fashion and beauty; interiors and location photography.
My client list includes: Marks and Spencer, Nestlé, John Lewis, Asda, Sainsbury's, Toshiba, Sun Microsystems, Braun, Egg, ICI, Sun Alliance, Swinton, Thomsons Holidays, Cunard, Filofax, Barclays Homes, Wickes, Sharpes, Lloyds TSB, Getty Images and numerous magazines.
I look forward to working with you!

M + 44 (0)7831 539 517
F + 44 (0)20 8892 1172
E styling@rosiehopper.co.uk
W www.rosiehopper.co.uk

Sarah Waller

Photographer: David Munns

Stylist/Art Director for food and lifestyle photography.

Recent clients include:
BBC
Boots
Peugeot
Tesco
Panasonic
Asda
Hamlyn Books
YOU Magazine

UK

M + 44 (0)7949 080 266
E waller_designs@yahoo.com

PROPS HIRE
including
modelmakers

Juicy Fruits

food stylist & model maker

t: 01223 290396
m: 07860 792082

www.juicyfruitsuk.com
contact: steven wheeler

Backgrounds

Unit 25 Waterside
44-48 Wharf Road
London N1 7UX
UK

T + 44 (0)20 7490 1181
F + 44 (0)20 7250 4104
W www.backgroundsprophire.co.uk

Opening Hours: Mon – Fri 09:30 – 17:30

Backgrounds specialises in the hire of
tableware and tabletops for food and still
life photography. We stock contemporary,
antique and commissioned pieces.

Tableware – ceramics, glass, metals,
cookware, cutlery, kitchen utensils, table
linen, fabrics and various accessories.

Tabletops – woods, stone, marbles, metals,
tiles, textured and painted surfaces.

Our props are used for editorial and
advertising work, packaging and
commercials.

China & Co

5000 sq. ft. of the best food and drink
props in London

Contact Paula Webster

2 C/D/E Macfarlane Road
Shepherds Bush
London W12 7JY
UK

T + 44 (0)20 8740 9588
F + 44 (0)20 8740 8873
E info@chinaandco.com
W www.chinaandco.com

WWW.*ContactACreative*.COM - COMPREHENSIVE SOURCE WEBSITE FOR ARTBUYERS

VIEW CONTACT DETAILS AND EXAMPLES OF WORK
FOR THE FOLLOWING RANGE OF PHOTOGRAPHIC SERVICES:

FOOD STYLISTS
PROPS & INTERIORS STYLISTS
HAIR & MAKE-UP
HIRE STUDIOS
HOME ECONOMISTS
LABS

LOCATION SERVICES
MODEL AGENCIES
MODEL MAKERS
PROPS HIRE
RETOUCHERS
SET BUILDERS

STUDIOS & LOCATION HOUSES

Angelspace

27-28 St. Albans Place
Angel, Islington
London N1 0NX
UK

T + 44 (0)20 7704 8803
E greg@angelstudio.freeserve.co.uk
W www.angelspace.co.uk

A smart, clean, air-conditioned studio (1000sqft wooden floor, 15ft ceiling) with a fully fitted open plan kitchen and separate make up & changing facilities. Profoto lighting, backgrounds and equipment on site make Angelspace perfect for shooting food and still life to fashion and portraiture. Located in Angel, it is also ideal for castings. Angelspace offers great value on day rates, equipment and catering.

Big Shed Studio Hire

Unit 18 Wheel Forge Way
Trafford Park
Manchester M17 1EH
UK

T + 44 (0)161 872 9222
F + 44 (0)161 872 9333
M + 44 (0)7831 434 068
E info@big-shed.co.uk
W www.big-shed.co.uk

A new build 4000 sq ft drive in studio suitable for HGV access with large L shaped cove plus a further 900 sq ft mezzanine studio. Full studio facilities availiable: lighting, hi res digital kit, Macs, 2 kitchens, shower, many props, meeting rooms, ample free parking and easy motorway links.

Ideal for large sets, food and products, fashion, automotive and TV or video productions. Please visit www.big-shed.co.uk for full details.

Boak Studio

Unit 10
17 Palmers Road
London E2 0SP
UK

T + 44 (0)20 8880 6611
F + 44 (0)20 8880 6644
M + 44 (0)7774 238 424
E kboak@tiscali.co.uk

Boak Studio has 1400 sq ft of easy configurable creative space. Secure off street parking. Ground floor access allows convenient equipment and product entry.
The open plan modern kitchen has a five ring gas hob and electric oven.
Facilities include camera stand, boom arm autopoles, polyboards.
Located near to the City and Docklands, both Bethnal Green and Mile End underground stations are a 7 minute walk away.

Dallington Studios

750 sq ft daylight studio. Ideal for food, lifestyle and castings. Open plan kitchen with gas hob & electric oven. Huge double height glass wall providing excellent light. Great location, ideal for labs, restaurants and good transport links.

Contact Nick.

1 Dallington Street
Clerkenwell
London EC1V 0BH
UK

T + 44 (0)20 7253 2863
F + 44 (0)20 7553 7740
E nick@nickcarman.com

Daylight Store

Daylight Store
Unit 311E
Safestore
5-10 Eastman Road
London W3 7YG
UK

T + 44 (0)7799 767 290
E info@thedaylightstore.co.uk
W www.thedaylightstore.co.uk

A beautiful daylight studio with a fantastic source of clean, natural light. It's an economical and compact space at 350 sq ft, which is ideal for budgets that aren't sky high. It has a fully equipped kitchen and secure 24 hour access. It also has full light stop and diffusion blinds and all white walls. Off street parking is free. More details and rates on website.

First Option Studio

FIRST OPTION STUDIO

Perseverance Works
London E2 8DD
UK

T + 44 (0)20 7739 0132
M + 44 (0)20 7729 7066
E studio@christinehanscomb.co.uk
W www.studiohirefirstoption.com

Studio - 30'w x 30'd x 20'ht daylight or full blackout. 3 phase power. Lab 2 mins away. 24 hour security in secure private courtyard. 9' Cambo studio stand available. Equipment hired in to order. 2 kitchens - largest 25'w x 20'd x 11'ht. fully equipped. Catering from light lunches to 4 course meals can be organised, Previous usage - includes advertising agencies - publishers - photographers for lifestyle, food, portraits - film production companies - pop promos - company conferences

Fish Tank Studio

Fish Tank Studio
153-159 Borough High Street
London SE1 1HR
UK

T + 44 (0)20 7357 7757
F + 44 (0)20 7357 8268
E fish.tank@btconnect.com
W www.fishtankstudio.com

Fish Tank Studio was first established in 1998. Set in the heart of SE1, this stunning daylight studio lies just 2 minutes from the famous Borough Market and London Bridge. The main aim of our studio is to provide a large and practical space, which is easily adaptable to your needs within a friendly and helpful atmosphere. All our facilities are listed on our website, but if you would like to find out more give us a call.

Halliford Studios

HALLIFORD FILM STUDIOS

- 2 Sound Stages
- Large Backlot
- 60 x 60 and 60 x 40 (both with Cyc)

- Construction
- Lighting
- Catering
- Off Street Parking
- Production Offices
- Dressing Rooms
- Make-up and Hairdressing

Contact: Callum Andrews or Suzanne May on
Telephone **01932 226341** Facsimile **01932 246336**

or visit our website @ **www.hallifordfilmstudios.co.uk**
Email **sales@hallifordstudios.com**

HALLIFORD STUDIOS LTD MANYGATE LANE SHEPPERTON MIDDX TW17 9EG

Halliford Studios Ltd
Manygate Lane
Shepperton
Middlesex TW17 9EG
UK

- **T** + 44 (0)1932 226 341
- **F** + 44 (0)1932 246 336
- **E** hallifordfilmstudios.co.uk
- **W** www.hallifordstudios.co.uk

The above stages are blacked out with infinity coves that can be painted to any colour. The studio is set in peaceful surroundings with gardens and plenty of parking. We have on site construction with many years' experience and the capabilities to deal with anything from the most demanding sets to the limbo pack shot. So if it is a blank canvas that you are looking for then please give us a call.

Hoxton Street Studios

BLOSSOM STREET

HOXTON STREET

FANSHAW STREET

12–18 Hoxton Street
London N1 6NG
UK

- **T** + 44 (0)20 7033 1984
- **F** + 44 (0)20 7033 1985
- **E** info@hoxtonstreetstudios.co.uk
- **W** www.hoxtonstreetstudios.co.uk

Location Works

locationworks.com

42 Old Compton Street
London W1D 4TX
UK

- **T** + 44 (0)20 7494 0888
- **F** + 44 (0)20 7287 2855
- **E** info@locationworks.com
- **W** www.locationworks.com

The largest and most comprehensive location library service in the UK.

While specialising in properties around the M25 our library covers the length and breadth of the country.

With over 1000 locations to choose from our dedicated team of co-ordinators can help you find what you are looking for quickly and efficiently.

With a wide variety of venues to choose from our experience in film, TV, stills and events, we can get the right location, whatever your budget or timeframe.

Meadows Farm Studios

Marlow Road
Henley-on-Thames
Oxon RG9 3AA, UK

- **T** + 44 (0)1491 577 789
- **F** + 44 (0)1491 410 504
- **E** studio@meadowsfarm.co.uk
- **W** www.meadowsfarmstudios.co.uk

You'll find us in an idyllic farm surrounding, away from the traffic hassles of London.

We offer a superb new kitchen, with loads of preparation space, in a lovely daylight/lifestyle studio… plus two client areas, and a beautiful garden to relax in. You'll be surprised at how easy it is to reach us, wherever you're coming from… By train from London Paddington you can reach us in less than an hour. By car we are 15 minutes away from the M4 and M40.
Beautiful location • Full kitchen • Daylight/lifestyle studio • 4 studios • Wi-fi network • Dedicated client areas • 2 bathrooms • Props

ndp

1 Pickering Street
Leeds LS12 2QG
West Yorkshire, UK

T + 44 (0)113 279 7175
F + 44 (0)113 279 5228
E info@ndp-leeds.co.uk
W www.ndp-leeds.co.uk

At ndp we have three studios available for
professional hire starting at £150 per day.

Whilst boasting a drive in studio with scoop
we also cater for those smaller scale projects.
All studios have make-up/changing facilities
available and studio 3 as seen above has an
adjacent kitchen area. We are situated just
1 mile from Leeds City Centre with ample free
parking. Equipment also available for hire.
Studio 1: Fashion/Press (Air conditioned)
Studio 2: Drive in with scoop/Sets etc
Studio 3: Food/Packshot
Contact us or visit our website for further details.

Photo-locations.com

29 Finlay Street
Fulham
London SW6 6HE
UK

T + 44 (0)20 7736 2929
F + 44 (0)20 7736 4633
M + 44 (0)7770 928 349
E info@photo-locations.com
W www.photo-locations.com

We are a friendly location company run
by a photographer and stylist. We specialise
in properties in the London area. Please visit
our website to view a selection or call us if
you have a specific need and we'll do our
best to find it.

Red Studios

Europa Studios
Studio 17
Victoria Road
West London NW10 6ND
UK

TF + 44 (0)20 8961 4991
E mailto@red-studios.com
W www.red-studios.com

- 2,000 sq ft daylight studio (47ft x 43ft)
- blackout • white gloss painted floor
- infinity cove (10ft high x15ft wide x17ft long)
- 3 phase power
- fully equipped kitchen (15ft x 11ft)
- make-up and changing room • lounge
- catering to order • lots of free parking
- just off the A40 in West London
- 1 minute walk to North Acton tube (Zone 2
Central Line) • roof facilities • set building
- Assistant

Studio Boardroom

Situated in a cobbled yard near Elephant
and Castle with rates to suit your budget.
600 sq. ft. of ground floor daylight (or
blackout) studio. Drive up to access and
parking. The mobile cooking unit can be
positioned anywhere in the studio to make
the best use of natural light or to create
different configurations either with the rest
of the kitchen or with other areas of the
studio. In house set builder, Broadband,
Cambo stand, Colorama stand, trestles,
poly boards, assorted studio boxes and
plinths etc.

22b Iliffe Yard
Kennington
London SE17 3QA, UK

Admin. 127 Honeywell Road SW11 6ED

T + 44 (0)20 7228 0225
F + 44 (0)20 7223 9740
M + 44 (0)7774 445 695
E jon.self@virgin.net
W www.sunnyhill1.co.uk

Sun Studios

6 Sun Studios
30 Warple Way
London W3 0RX
UK

T + 44 (0)20 8749 5888
E simon@simonsmithphotography.com
W www.simonsmithphotography.com

West London food & still life hire studio with digital facilities. 900 sq ft studio with fully equipped kitchen (2 ovens, fridges and freezers). Large selection of props also available to hire. Situated between Acton, Chiswick and Shepherd's Bush. Can be hired as studio only or with Sinar digital set up. Contact Simon Smith.

Tattersall Love

40 Langham Street
London W1W 7AS
UK

T + 44 (0)20 7637 5737
F + 44 (0)20 7637 5747
E location@tattersall-love.com
W www.tattersall-love.com

From the unusual and often quirky, to the modern and sleek, we represent locations both in the UK and abroad. We can cater for all photographic requirements, including location finding, production, catering and casting by a small and friendly team.

Tim White Studio Hire

London SW6 5EA
UK

T + 44 (0)20 7736 8845
E timwhitefoto@clara.co.uk

Working studio for hire.

700sq ft

*£145 per day
£15/hour overtime after 7.30pm*

Minimum height 11ft sloping up to 13ft

Small model room

Warm air heating, 20KW power.

Floating flat 10ftx10ft.

Blackout blinds.

Excellent security.

Very close to Calumet Heathmans Road.

Contact Tim White

West Point Studios

3c Westpoint
36-37 Warple Way
London W3 0RG
UK

T + 44 (0)20 8749 9911
M + 44 (0)7831 751 712
E amanda@food-photography.co.uk
W www.amandaheywood.co.uk

Beautiful open plan 1000 sq ft daylight studio with fully equipped kitchen and stunning views across London East & West

Facilities include 2 ovens, 2 fridges, freezer & dishwasher • Shuttered windows • 9ft Cambo stand • Wireless Broadband • Comfortable client area • Darkroom • On street parking • Props.

Situated between Acton, Chiswick & Shepherds Bush. Ideal for Food, Still Life, People, TV Castings & Interviews.

*Also available for Hire
HMI, Tungsten & Strobe Flash • Broadcast AVID & FCP edit suite with Beta SP, DVCam & Digital Betacam • Beach Hut located on the South Coast.*

IMAGE LIBRARIES

Turn over for image libraries, visit our website for more services

FOODPHOTOGRAPHERS.COM

fabfood*pix*.com

www.fabfoodpix.com
+44(0)20 8211 9922
info@fabfoodpix.com

food image library

fabfood*pix*.com

www.fabfoodpix.com
+44(0)20 8211 9922
info@fabfoodpix.com

food image library

foodfolio

Foodfolio is one of the world's leading producers of rights managed stock food and drink photography. Foodfolio brings the best in contemporary food and beverage photography direct to your desktop. We specialise in high resolution images for design, advertising, editorial, promotion and multimedia.

www.foodfolio.com
+44 (0) 020 7729 8460
info@foodfolio.com

food&drink
photos.com

Foodanddrinkphotos is the latest and most exciting rights-protected food and drink image library.

Our site has been specifically created to meet the growing client demand for more up to date, modern food and drink photography.

Our new and constantly expanding collection already offers a wide range of both food and drink related images showcasing the work of an elite group of leading food and drink photographers. And, because we are new, our images are genuinely fresh and innovative with a more contemporary style.

Not only do we offer a fresh approach to classic images of raw ingredients, cooked dishes and popular drinks, but our collection also includes an inspirational selection of highly creative, conceptual photography.

www.foodanddrinkphotos.com
Telephone 020 8740 6610

FOOD & DRINK

PHOTOGRAPHERS INDEX

8-9

Frank Adam

4 Empress Mews
Kenbury Street
London SE5 9BT
UK

T + 44 (0)20 7738 6901
E frank@frankadamphoto.com
W www.frankadamphoto.com
W www.foodphotographers.com/Frank
Adam

10-11

Chris Alack

37 Mirabel Road
Fulham
London SW6 7EQ
UK

T + 44 (0)20 7610 3454
F + 44 (0)20 7381 1560
M + 44 (0)7785 717 625
E chris@ulack.co.uk
W www.foodphotographers.com/Chris
Alack

12-13

Matthew Barlow

UK

T + 44 (0)20 7697 8291
F + 44 (0)20 7619 9051
M + 44 (0)7836 594 580
W www.foodphotographers.com/
MatthewBarlow

Agent: Germaine Walker
T + 44 (0)20 7697 8291
E matthew@germaine.co.uk
W www.germaine.co.uk

14-15

Chris Biggs

167-169 Great Portland Street
London W1W 5PF
UK

T + 44 (0)20 7323 6606
F + 44 (0)20 7636 6606
E laura@chrisbiggs.co.uk
W www.chrisbiggs.co.uk
W www.foodphotographers.com/
ChrisBiggs

16-17

Tim Bowden

Tim Bowden Photography Ltd
Lower Ground Floor
7 Mallow Street
London EC1Y 8RQ
UK

T + 44 (0))20 7490 3500
F + 44 (0)20 7253 6676
E t.bowden@netcomuk.co.uk
W www.timbowdenfood.co.uk
W www.foodphotographers.com/
TimBowden

18-19

Clive Bozzard-Hill

Represented by Rosie Deckett
UK

T + 44 (0)20 8255 1574
M + 44 (0)7973 193 071
E rosiebeckett@mac.com
W www.bozza-uk.com
W www.foodphotographers.com/
CliveBozzardHill

20-21

Heather Brown

Floor 1, Mill 1
Mabgate Mills
Macauley Street
Leeds LS9 7DZ
UK

T + 44 (0)1132 44 88 55
W www.foodphotographers.com/Heather
Brown

22-23

Gerrit Buntrock

Atlantic Studios
1 Warple Mews
Warple Way
London W3 0RF
UK

T + 44 (0)20 8749 1797
F + 44 (0)20 8742 9873
E info@gerritbuntrock.com
W www.gerritbuntrock.com
W www.foodphotographers.com/
GerritBuntrock

24 25

James Butler

Higher Stennack Farm
Troon, Camborne
Cornwall TR14 9JS
UK

T + 44 (0)1209 832 993
M + 44 (0)7855 374 031
E butlerpenryn@btconnect.com
W imagingcornwall.co.uk
W www.foodphotographers.com/
JamesButler

26-27

Nick Carman

UK

T + 44 (0)20 7253 2863
F + 44 (0)20 7553 7740
E nick@nickcarman.com
W www.nickcarman.com
W www.foodphotographers.com/
NickCarman

28-29

Peter Cassidy

Apt. 7
The Old Aero Works
17 Hatton Street
London NW8 8PL
UK

T/F + 44 (0)20 7258 0/05
M + 44 (0)7976 739 915
E petecassidy@excite.com
W www.foodphotographers.com/Peter
Cassidy

30-31

Jean Cazals

27 Barlby Road
London W10 6AN
UK

T + 44 (0)20 7912 1259
F + 44 (0)20 7912 1260
M + 44 (0)7860 777 143
E info@jeancazals.net
W www.jeancazals.net

See also Contact Food & Drink
5, 6, 7, 8, 9, 10
W www.foodphotographers.com/
JeanCazals

80-81

Lis Parsons

Middle Floor Studio
13 Morecambe Street
London SE17 1DX
UK

T + 44 (0)7932 013 751
E lis@lisparsonsphotography.co.uk
W www.lisparsonsphotography.co.uk
W www.foodphotographers.com/LisParsons

82-83

Simon Pask

UK

T + 44 (0)20 7251 2414
F + 44 (0)20 7490 2392
E simon@simonpask.com
W www.simonpask.com
W www.foodphotographers.com/
SimonPask

84-85

Steve Payne

First Floor
Building D
The Chocolate Factory
Clarendon Road
London N22 6XJ
UK

TF + 44 (0)20 8889 6609
M + 44 (0)7850 329 691
E stevepaynephotog@btconnect.com
W www.stevepaynephotography.co.uk
W www.foodphotographers.com/
StevePayne

86-87

Graham Precey

Studio Four
Sun Studios
30 Warple Way
London W3 0RX
UK

T + 44 (0)20 8762 9993
F + 44 (0)20 8762 9994
E graham@precey.com
W www.precey.com
W www.foodphotographers.com/
GrahamPrecey

88-89

Gareth Sambidge

Represented @ Process
UK

T + 44 (0)20 7277 8400
M + 44 (0)7950 311 425
E kim@processphotography.com
W www.processphotography.com
W www.foodphotographers.com/
GarethSambidge

90-91

Toby Scott

6 Sun Studios
30 Warple Way
London W3 0RX
UK

T + 44 (0)20 8749 5888
F + 44 (0)20 8749 1223
M + 44 (0)7961 189 709
E toby@tobyscottphotography.com
W www.tobyscottphotography.com
W www.foodphotographers.com/
TobyScott

92-93

Andy Seymour

82 Princedale Road
Holland Park
London W11 4NL
UK

T + 44 (0)20 7221 2021
F + 44 (0)20 7792 0702
E andy@andyseymour.co.uk
W www.andyseymour.co.uk
W www.foodphotographers.com/
AndySeymour

94-95

shootingfood

UK

T + 44 (0)1242 513 405
F + 44 (0)1242 513 446
E rm@shootingfood.com
W www.shootingfood.com
W www.foodphotographers.com/shooting
food

96-97

Simon Smith

6 Sun Studios
30 Warple Way
London W3 0RX
UK

T + 44 (0)20 8749 5888
F + 44 (0)20 8749 1223
M + 44 (0)7976 258 660
E simon@simonsmithphotography.com
W www.simonsmithphotography.com
W www.foodphotographers.com/
SimonSmith

Digital still life photographer specialising
in food and drink. West London studio
encompasses both daylight 'lifestyle' and
still life studios (both with kitchens).
Types of work undertaken include
advertising, editorial, packaging and
public relations.

Clients include:
Asda, BBC Books & Magazines, Bernard
Matthews, Birds Eye Wall's, Britvic,
Crosse & Blackwell, Dolmio, Dorling
Kindersley, EMAP, Harper Collins, Heinz,
Hovis, IPC, KFC, Linda McCartney, Marks
& Spencer, McDonald's, McDougalls,
McVitie's, National Magazines, Nestlé,
Sainsbury's, Schwartz, Seafish, Shloer,
Somerfield, Tate & Lyle, Tesco, Wild Bean
Café.

98-99

Stuart West
Photographer

UK

M + 44 (0)7711 356 633
E stuartwest@btinternet.com
W www.foodphotographers.com/
StuartWest

www.foodphotographers.com

online portfolios for all of these specialist food photographers

CREATIVES IN CONTACT

www.**contact**-uk.com

*creatives in contact **world—wide***